Series editor: CAROL BARRATT

CLASSIC OPERA

Arranged for piano solo by Barrie Carson Turner

Chester Music

(A division of Music Sales Limited)
8/9 Frith Street, London W1V 5TZ

Contents

Chorus of Hebrew Slaves

from *Nabucco*

Giuseppe Verdi (1813–1901)

'Leise, leise'
from *Der Freischütz*

Carl Maria von Weber (1786-1826)

5

The 'Anvil' Chorus
from *Il Trovatore*
'Look, the dark night approaches'

Giuseppe Verdi (1813-1901)

'Là, ci darem la mano'
from *Don Giovanni*
'There, let us join hands'

Wolfgang Amadeus Mozart (1756-1791)

Che gelida manina
from *La Bohème*

'How cold your little hand is'

Giacomo Puccini (1858-1924)

Barcarolle
from *The Tales of Hoffmann*

Jacques Offenbach (1819-1880)

D.C. al ⊕ Coda ⊕ CODA

11

Minuet
from *Berenice*

George Frederic Handel (1685-1759)

The Birdcatcher's Song

from *The Magic Flute*

'Der Vogelfänger bin ich ja'

Wolfgang Amadeus Mozart (1756-1791)

14

Non più andrai
from *The Marriage of Figaro*

Wolfgang Amadeus Mozart (1756-1791)

Evening Prayer
from *Hansel and Gretel*

'Abends will ich schlafen gehn'
'When at night I go to sleep'

Engelbert Humperdinck (1854-1921)

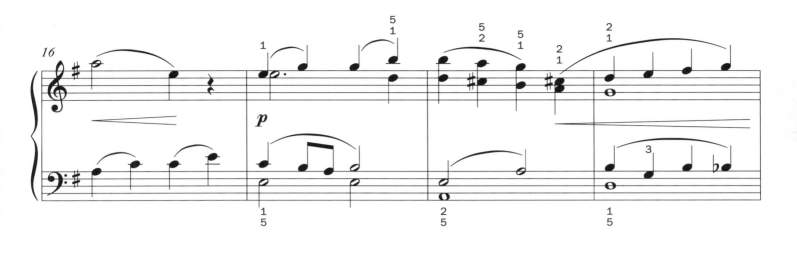

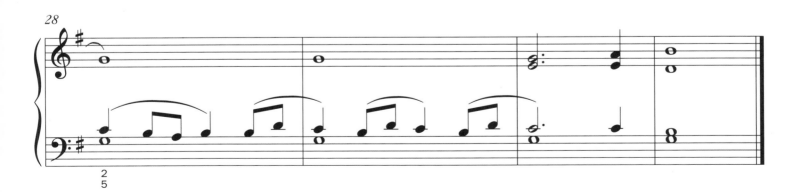

Air
from *Martha*
'M'appari'

Friedrich von Flotow (1812-1883)

18

19

Treulich geführt

(Bridal March)
from *Lohengrin*

Richard Wagner (1813-1883)

Mässig bewegt
(Moderately)

20

D.C. al ⊕ Coda   ⊕ CODA

Voi, che sapete

from *The Marriage of Figaro*

'You who have knowledge'

Wolfgang Amadeus Mozart (1756-1791)

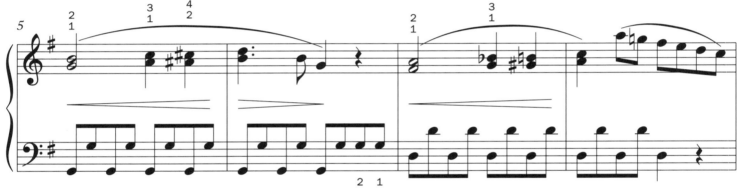

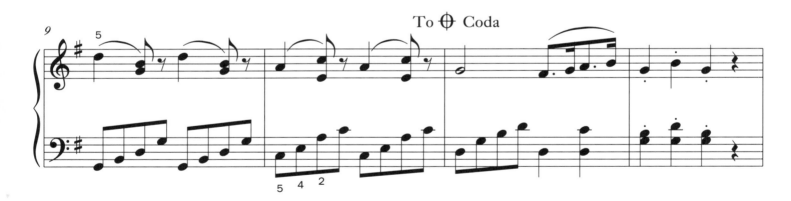

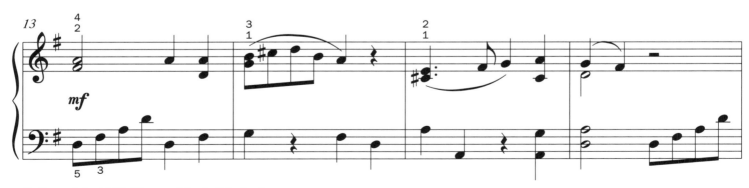

D.C. al ⊕ Coda

⊕ CODA

Vissi d'arte
from *Tosca*
'I lived for art'

Giacomo Puccini (1858-1924)

Andante lento appassionato

Flower Duet

from *Lakmé*

'Viens, Mallika'

Léo Delibes (1836-1891)

Andantino con moto

26

Duet
from *The Pearl Fishers*
'Au fond du temple saint'

Georges Bizet (1838-1875)

Habanera
from *Carmen*
'L'amour est un oiseau rebelle'

Georges Bizet (1838-1875)

Allegro quasi andantino

* ♩♩♩ original rhythm
_3_

30